MW00696335

Ben Has to Go!

by Samantha Montgomery
illustrated by Ann Iosa

SCHOOL PUBLISHERS

Copyright © by Harcourt, Inc.

All rights reserved. No part of this publication may be reproduced or transmitted in any form or by any means, electronic or mechanical, including photocopy, recording, or any information storage and retrieval system, without permission in writing from the publisher.

Requests for permission to make copies of any part of the work should be addressed to School Permissions and Copyrights, Harcourt, Inc., 6277 Sea Harbor Drive, Orlando, Florida 32887–6777. Fax: 407-345-2418.

HARCOURT and the Harcourt Logo are trademarks of Harcourt, Inc., registered in the United States of America and/or other jurisdictions.

Printed in Mexico

ISBN-13: 978-0-15-358474-9
ISBN-10: 0-15-358474-2

Ordering Options
ISBN 10: 0-15-358357-6 (Grade K Advanced-Level Collection)
ISBN 13: 978-0-15-358357-5 (Grade K Advanced-Level Collection)
ISBN 10: 0-15-360727-0 (package of 5)
ISBN 13: 978-0-15-360727-1 (package of 5)

If you have received these materials as examination copies free of charge, Harcourt School Publishers retains title to the materials and they may not be resold. Resale of examination copies is strictly prohibited and is illegal.

Possession of this publication in print format does not entitle users to convert this publication, or any portion of it, into electronic format.

3 4 5 6 7 8 9 10   050   15 14 13 12 11 10 09 08

This is Ben and his sax.

He has to go play his sax.

Ben will toss his sax in the van.

Sid will get him to his show.

"This van will not go," said Ben.

"I can not fix it. We do not have gas.

What can we do?"

"We can get a cab," said Sid.

Ben and Sid run to get a cab.

They want a cab to come,

but one will not come.

What can Ben and Sid do?

What can Ben and Sid do?

Ben can see a bus.

"The bus will get us there, Sid!"

said Ben.

"Hop in!" said the man on the bus.

"We are Ben and Sid," said Ben.

"Ben has to play in a show," said Sid.

"Can you get us there?" said Ben.

"Yes, I can," said the man.

"This bus will get you there."

Here they are.

Sid will see Ben play in the band.

He will see Ben play jazz on his sax.